THE PHANTOM BULLY

by *New York Times* bestselling author
Jeffrey Brown

Scholastic Inc.

Thanks to everyone who helped make this series a great experience to create, and a better story to read: Joanne, Frank, Leland, Carol, JW Rinzler, and everyone else at Lucasfilm; Marc, Chris, Brett, Steve, Phoebe, and all my other editors, publishers, and colleagues; my friends and family, especially Jennifer, Oscar, and Simon; all the readers who've been so supportive and responsive; and everyone at Scholastic who got this book out into the world in the best shape possible. Finally, extra special thanks to Rex Ogle, for being an editor when he needed to be, a friend when I needed him to be, and quite often both at once.

www.starwars.com
www.scholastic.com

Published by Scholastic Inc., *Publishers since 1920.* SCHOLASTIC and associated logos are trademarks and/or registered trademarks of Scholastic Inc.

The publisher does not have any control over and does not assume any responsibility for author or third-party websites or their content.

Library of Congress Control Number Available

ISBN 978-0-545-85128-2

10 9 8 7 6 5 4 3 2   15 16 17 18 19

Printed in the U.S.A.   23
This edition first printing 2015

A long time ago in a galaxy far, far away....

There was a boy named Roan Novachez (that's me), who was FINALLY becoming a REAL pilot at JEDI ACADEMY! Now he's starting his final year there, and it's probably going to be REALLY, REALLY hard, but it's also going to be really AWESOME!

Me at the end of last year

Me at the start of this year!

7

WELCOME BACK AGAIN TO JEDI ACADEMY

As students return for their final year at Jedi Academy on the planet Coruscant, their Padawan training will enter a new and exciting phase. Each Padawan will be paired with a Jedi mentor for individual instruction. They will also choose a specialized area of focus, such as healing, piloting, or farming. Padawans will finish the year well-prepared to continue on their path to become Jedi.

This year, Padawans will focus on their unique abilities in a number of ways, including the class talent show. Students will have the chance to show off their favorite hobbies and hidden skills. The individual strengths

of each student will also be measured in the Padawan Obstacle Challenge Trial, where teams of students must work together to solve problems and get through barriers using their strongest skills. In order to finish their training at Jedi Academy, Padawans must also complete the Jedi Labyrinth Trial

by finding their way through a maze while defeating other students in lightsaber duels.

PENTADAY

This summer break was a lot shorter than last year. At least, it seems that way. It helps that Gaiana and I have been talking and writing to each other all summer. Pasha also came to stay with me for a few days. I thought he was going to be really bored, but he

said Tatooine is so different from where he grew up, it was really fun for him. I leave for school next week already, and this time I think I finally really know for sure what I'm doing. Plus, I'm not going to get cocky like last year, especially since I have

to work with Mr. G. for my one-on-one training. As long as I can make it through, it's okay if it's not perfect. Unless Mr. G. ends up making me as grumpy as he always is...

STUDENT: ROAN NOVACHEZ	
LEVEL: PADAWAN	SEMESTER: FIVE
HOMEROOM: MASTER YODA	
CLASS SCHEDULE	

0730 - 0850: HABITS OF USING THE FORCE
Master Yoda will help students make the Force a part of their everyday routines.

0900 - 0950: PRACTICAL MATH
Mrs. Pilton will show students how to apply math skills to useful tasks, such as buying things.

1000 - 1050: CREATIVE WRITING
Under the guidance of Librarian Lackbar, students will develop expressive new writing.

1100 - 1150: ETHICS OF JEDI MIND TRICKS
Principal Mar will teach students principles to consider before attempting mind tricks.

1200 - 1300: LUNCH BREAK

1300 - 1350: INDEPENDENT STUDY I
Students will spend intense periods working closely with their assigned Jedi mentor.

1400 - 1450: LIGHTSABER ACROBATICS
Mr. Garfield will team up with Kitmum to teach students more dynamic moves for lightsaber duels.

1500 - 1550: ADVANCED STAR PILOT TRAINING
Mr. Garfield will train students using star pilot simulators of increasing difficulty.

GOOD. IT'S GOING TO BE HARD ENOUGH TO TRAIN YOU, WITHOUT YOUR USUAL MISBEHAVING.

Must...not... respond!

Ugh. I can't believe he's going to be my Jedi mentor all year.

Who's your Jedi mentor, Gaiana?

Librarian Lackbar.

Mine's Principal Mar. I've got some new Jedi...

I have M'Ba-Tee, the Jedi who visited last year.

I wonder who's training with Master Yoda?

Guess.

What?! No way!

Heh heh! Good to work with you, it will be, Cyrus.

You guys would tell me if Jedi Academy was conspiring against me, right?

Of course! Sure!

Unless we were in on it...

Yeah.

Just kidding!

16

The Padawan Observer

EDITED BY THE STUDENTS OF JEDI ACADEMY · Vol. MXIV #1

WELCOME BACK ALREADY!

Another year at Jedi Academy has begun after what some students describe as a long summer break. "It seems like FOREVER since I've seen my friends!" exclaimed an excited Shi-Fara. Teachers, however, had a different view. "Hmph," Mr. Garfield stated. "Why even send these kids home every summer if they're going to come back so soon?" Padawans enjoyed an all-school picnic where

they met their independent study Jedi mentors, many who are former teachers and students from the Coruscant Campus. Gammy says there is leftover Potato Slug Salad if anyone would like more to take home.

TRIDAY

I was going to try and stay positive in this journal entry because I'm happy to be back at Jedi Academy and seeing Gaiana and Pasha, but AUGGGGGGGHHHHHHH, MR.G.! All of us spent time meeting with our individual Jedi mentors and already Mr.G. is making it impossible for me.

> **WHAT DO YOU WANT?**
>
> **You asked me to meet with you?**
>
> **YOU WANT ME TO ASK YOU TO MEET WITH ME?**
>
> **Hunh?**

I thought <u>Master Yoda</u> was supposed to be the wise mystic with confusing sayings! The two classes after my independent study are with Mr.G., too. It's going to be a long school year. It won't be so bad, since I have good friends to relax with. We decided we're going to have a board game night once a

week. Gaiana and I were on the same team and won the first game, which is totally the perfect start to the semester!

Yesterday, we met a new transfer student in class. I remember when I was the "new kid." It was rough! The new girl, Lilly, is REALLY good using the Force, though. She even beat Cyrus in lightsaber fencing class. Even Mr.G. was impressed, and of course it was a perfect ~~opportunity~~ opportunity for him to point out how much

> Ha! I guess you shouldn't have been going easy on her.

> I wasn't!

training **I** still need. Lilly felt bad about Mr.G. comparing me to her, and said she was just trying to do her best, but we told her not to worry. That's how Mr.G. always is. Gaiana invited Lilly to sit with us at lunch. We found out she's vegetarian and doesn't eat any meat. The strange thing about that is she was vegetarian BEFORE she even tried Gammy's cooking!

> Hey! Why doesn't your pasta have eye-meatballs?

> Maybe we should be vegetarian.

Each Padawan will focus on their own specific area of study this year. What are you studying?

POSTED BY L. LACKBAR

 I'm going to study music.

 I'm studying dance, we should work together! Er, individually as a team?

 I'm focusing on interactions between the Force and nature.

 I think you'll be a natural at that!

 "Natural?" I get it, ha! Let me guess your focus...Star pilot?

 I figured everyone probably knew that already!

 I didn't. I thought you'd focus on being a klutz.

 Why don't YOU focus on being positive instead of negative, Cronah?

 Yeah, aren't you still on academic probation? You should be nicer.

 Lightsaber fencing.

That was my choice, too! Is that allowed?

DUODAY

I've been having a lot of fun with Gaiana in class, because we're study partners, but Cronah is trying to ruin it. He even got Ronald to start making fun of me. Ever since I came to Jedi Academy, Cronah and his friends have been out to get me. I

> Hey, Roan! We have a new name for you and Gaiana. Know what it is?

> No, what?

> Groan.

> Ha ha ha!

would say it's because HE likes Gaiana, but I don't think Cronah likes ANYONE. Last year, I probably would've gotten advice from Yoda (about dealing with Cronah, not about Gaiana). I can't talk to Yoda about anything lately, because he's spending a lot of time as Cyrus's individual instructor. I can't talk to Mr. G., that's for sure! That's why Pasha's such a great friend — we can talk about anything. He's been dating Shi-Fara a while, so he has lots of good advice. Like, I should just ignore Cronah... I think I already knew that, too!

> Uh, Mr. G., can I talk to you about something personal?

> NO. HMPH.

MIND TRICKS

A Jedi can use the Force to influence the behavior of others

- When using the Force for mind tricks, make sure you wave your hand properly.

Hand movement should be subtle ←

Too much! →

- Mind tricks should never be used for profit or gain.

- Using mind tricks on your friends will lead to you not having any friends to use mind tricks on.

- Begin by practicing mind tricks on your pets.

Sit!

I said, sit!

C'mon, sit!

* If the ice cream shop is out of the flavor you're looking for, using mind tricks to make them say they aren't out of that flavor will not make the flavor appear.

Things Yoda communicated to us this week

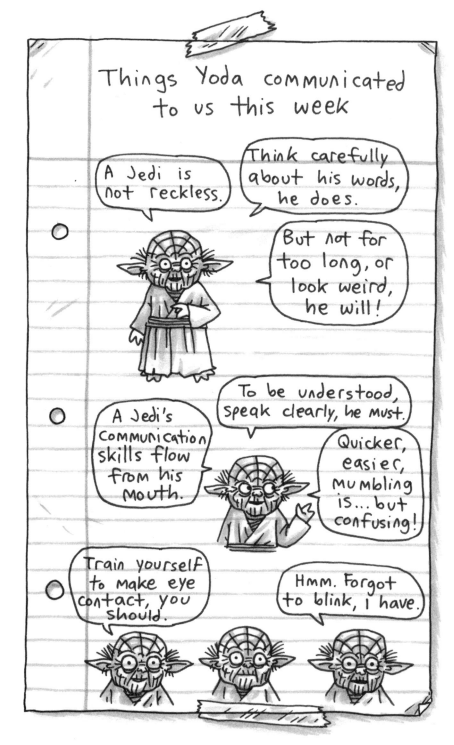

A Jedi is not reckless.

Think carefully about his words, he does.

But not for too long, or look weird, he will!

To be understood, speak clearly, he must.

A Jedi's communication skills flow from his mouth.

Quicker, easier, mumbling is... but confusing!

Train yourself to make eye contact, you should.

Hmm. Forgot to blink, I have.

FROM: master_yoda_642
TO: Padawan Class Group
SUBJECT: Important Field Trip
Information

OPTIONS
◁ REPLY
▷ FORWARD
▣ PRINT
◍ POST TO HOLOBOOK

WHEN: WEEK THREE
WHERE: THE PLANET NABOO
PURPOSE: To study environmental impact by various societies on different habitats, and learn conservation strategies using the Force.

ACTIVITIES: Students will observe wildlife in its natural habitat and captivity, swim in Lake Paonga, and visit the Gungan Sacred Place.

NOTES: Students should plan on taking notes for post-field trip essay writing. Students should not worry about sando aqua monsters, which hardly ever get near the student swimming area.

CHAPERONES: Yoda, Librarian Lackbar, Kitmum, and RW-22.

ITEMS TO BRING: Swimsuit, sunscreen, swim goggles, waterproof notebook, binoculars, scuba gear, towel.*

*Make sure towel is not waterproof or it will not dry you off.

You can see how these grass plains are still affected by the nearby city of Theed, while areas like Lake Country are nearly untouched.

I better take some notes...

A good student takes lots of notes.

But make eye contact and nod head so she knows I'm listening.

Mm-hm.

Repeat information to remember it better. So Lake Country is only accessible by speeder.

Remember to ask questions. How do they make sure people don't build on the plains?

Roan, you look tired... is this too much walking?

No... paying attention is exhausting!

MONODAY

Naboo is Gaiana's favorite planet to visit, so the field trip has been fun. Yesterday we visited the Gungan Sacred Place. It didn't look sacred to us, because it was all ruins grown over with plants in a swamp. Master Yoda explained that respect for nature is maybe part of what makes it sacred, although not even our Gungan guide knew why the place was sacred. It still looked really cool! Tomorrow, we're going swimming in Lake Paonga. I'm kind of nervous, because I've only ever swam in a swimming pool before.

29

HEXADAY

Master Yoda decided we should do team-building exercises at the lake, so we had swimming relay races. My team wasn't doing well, because I'm not a great swimmer. Unless I'm compared to other kids on Tatooine, since there's

> Train yourself to let go of everything you fear getting wet.

> Leave your dry clothes and shoes on the shore, you should!

no water there! My team didn't get mad at me, though, they just started coming up with funny swim styles, which was way better. I started feeling like the "new kid" again, until we went to the shaaks farm. Our Gungan guide showed us how to ride the shaaks, and it isn't that different from riding dewbacks on Tatooine. I even gave Lilly some tips until she got the hang of it. Then she started

> She's kind of a show-off.

> Yeah. I like her.

> Guys! Try this!

doing tricks! Everyone was impressed. Again. She's totally the coolest kid at our school now.

Before we went to the Naboo Zoo, Gaiana seemed really quiet. After what happened last year, I decided I should just talk to her. At least then I'd know if she was mad at me. It turned out she was actually feeling insecure, because Lilly is good at everything and everyone likes her. So it made Gaiana feel weird when I was helping Lilly out with riding the shaaks. I told Gaiana I was just trying to be more helpful now, like Pasha was with Gaiana's dad last year. She said I was sweet. She even tried to kiss me! On the cheek. But I turned my head by accident, so she ended up

Huh?

Ack! Pfft! Hair!

kissing my hair instead. She laughed, so it was okay. At the zoo, she showed me around. When we saw the voorpaks, the zookeepers asked if we wanted to care for one at Jedi Academy again. Voorpee is coming back with us! I'm going to make sure nothing happens to him this time.

I don't think this is Voorpee...

How can you tell it's not him?

Um, it's a her!

Oh!

33

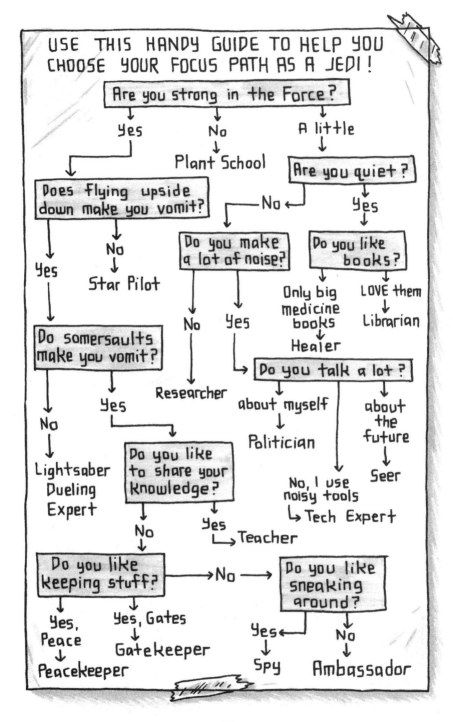

Things Mr. G. said to me this week

A LITTLE HARD WORK NEVER HURTS.

HMPH. UNLESS YOU'RE DOING IT WRONG.

IT MIGHT HURT A LOT, ACTUALLY.

ALL WORK AND NO PLAY WILL ACTUALLY MAKE YOU THE BEST AT WHAT YOU DO.

SO NO PLAYING.

EVER.

WORK SMARTER, NOT HARDER.

ESPECIALLY IF YOU DON'T KNOW WHAT YOU'RE DOING. HMPH.

＊ This week's "Hmph" count: 453

straighten

Fidget

Ready for our double date, Roan?

No, but if we don't go now I'm going to be all sweaty!

Wait! What are those?!

Flowers.

Oh, no! I didn't get any...

Don't worry, I got you covered!

Phew, thanks!

Hey, Gaiana!

Hey, Shi-Fara!

Hey, guys!

I hope it's okay if someone else comes along?

BWEET?

Oh, my! I wasn't planning on it, but RW-22 and I would be honored to accompany you!

BLOOP!

Oh, er, T-P30, we meant...

This will be delightful, I am so happy!

BEEP BOOP TWEET!

Oh, no! I forgot my wallet!

It's okay, I'll cover you, Roan.

Oh, thanks...

I'm so full!

We don't have to be back to our dorms for an hour. What should we do?

If I may suggest, the soccer field bleachers offer a splendid view of the sunset.

But we need a teacher to go there after school hours.

I suppose if I take you, that would be allowed, as long as we leave right after.

Did you guys know Lilly's team won the Adega System Soccer Championship?

Really?

Our team almost made regionals once!

QUADDAY

My first official date with Gaiana last night was awesome! I didn't spill anything on myself or Gaiana, I didn't say anything embarrassing, and I didn't accidentally ruin it. Gaiana is funny and cute and smart. She's also the nicest person I've ever met. The weird part of our date was that Cyrus came along with Lilly. And he was super nice! Maybe now that he's working with Master Yoda, Cyrus does want to focus on being a Jedi instead of being a jerk. Or he's just behaving because he's on probation. He seemed nice last year, and ended up totally trying to ruin my year. So I need to be careful, because I wouldn't be surprised if this was part of some plan he has with Cronah. Cronah seems in an even worse mood than usual lately — if that's even possible. This morning he totally tried to trip me, and most of the time he's just saying stuff. Maybe Cronah will start pretending to be nice like Cyrus.

Roan, what do you think of the new star pilot simulator software? Any tips?

Oops! Sorry, Roan.

Hey!

PADAWANS IN THE NEWS

- Jedi Academy student Pasha contributed to a research paper by his father, published in the new issue of Jedi Archaeology.
- Transfer student Lilly was honored with a plaque and restaurant gift certificate for her contributions last year to the Jedi Academy Ossus Campus debate team.
- A profile of student Council president Ronald Rinzler was featured in the Coruscant Senate Bulletin.

Ewok Pilot

By Roan Novachez

Ewok Pilot and Jawa Pilot, did you finish your Patrol Report Paperwork?

Chak!

Ibana!

THE PADAWAN OBSERVER   VOL. MXIV #3

HOLOSEARCH

You searched for....'Roan Novachez'
0 results found.
REFINE YOUR SEARCH.

Did you mean....'Ronto'?
31,100 results found [.35 Galactic
                              standard seconds]

RONTO
Strong but docile beasts of burden,
Rontos are commonly used by
the Jawas of Tatooine for...

RONTO FOR SALE
Elderly Ronto for sale. Still works
hard but is really, really slow...

RONTO CENTRAL
Your source for your Ronto supplies...

Images for...'Ronto'

TRIDAY

I felt really bad about what Cronah did to our substitute teacher, Mr. Vendo, yesterday. Not just because it was mean, but because I didn't say anything. At first, nobody said anything, but then Gaiana and Lilly did. Gaiana is always good like that. I wish I could learn to stand up for other people like she does, but even when I think of saying

Can we NOT have Cronah teach? I want to actually learn today.

You don't have to be such a jerk, Cronah, geez.

something, I don't, and by the time I'm ready to speak up, it's too late. Like, weeks late. I did tell Gaiana it was good of her right away. One thing she and I have been doing together is taking care of Voorpee. The little voorpak has really warmed up to me, even after last year's drama. I'm sure his liking me has nothing to do with the extra treats I've been feeding to him.

He really likes you! It's like he wants to live in your pocket...

Yeah, heh heh!

HEXADAY

Someone took my backpack and I KNOW it was CRONAH! If hate wasn't the path to the dark side, I would say I hate him, but instead I'll say I really, really, really, really, don't like Cronah. I would've thought it was him anyway, since he keeps saying stuff that totally shows he's in on the prank. Pasha agrees that it was

Roan, did you just get BACK from somewhere?

Huh?

It felt like you were MISSING.

Class seemed less PACKed than usual.

probably Cronah, but he, Bill, and Egon all told me not to worry, and they'll help me look for it. Gaiana and Shi-Fara even offered to let me use one of their bags until I find mine. Having friends rules. At least my journal wasn't in my backpack— that would've been a DISASTER. Especially if Cronah was reading it. It's still kind of a disaster, because all of my star pilot training notes and workbook were in it. I'm going to have to work extra hard to make up all of that work. I know Mr.G. will have ZERO sympathy for me.

I know Cronah took my backpack!

Hmmm... he wouldn't really still have the same locker combination after last year, would he?

Aha!

CLICK!

Smells like old socks! Let's see... ew, sticky...

I don't see it...

MR. NOVACHEZ! WHAT ARE YOU DOING? IS THAT YOUR LOCKER?

Uh-oh!

Uh, no, it's Cronah's, I think he took my backpack and—

YOU NEED TO LEARN TO BE RESPONSIBLE FOR YOUR THINGS, ROAN.

AND YOU NEED TO LEARN TO NOT MESS WITH OTHER PEOPLE'S BELONGINGS. I THINK DETENTION IS IN ORDER HERE.

But—

HMPH.

DUODAY

Well, my backpack was found. Fortunately, everything was still in it! UNfortunately, whoever took it filled it with leftover food and put it under a table in the cafeteria. For a minute, I got excited, because I realized there's a Force ability where you can sense the history of an object, and Silva's focusing on being a detective for his individual training. He couldn't sense

> Let's see... I sense... moldy grainmush... it was in a bowl. And there's some pickled zog... half eaten.

> Ew, gross!

who took it, though, because the backpack was too messy. I feel stupid for not redoing all my star pilot training homework already. I was doing it kind of slowly because I was hoping it would be inside whenever I found my backpack. I'm still sure Cronah did it, but maybe he had help...

The Usual Suspects ⟶

It's hard enough getting all of my own work done without having other people asking me to do work for them. I don't know why Ronald tries to get ME to do all his work for him. He's focusing on politics with his Kaminoan Jedi mentor, and asked me to illustrate the essay he's writing. I told him I didn't have time, and Ronald acted annoyed and grumbled

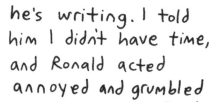

C'mon, Big Guy! You're my only hope for an "A"!

about me drawing stuff for Gaiana. First, Gaiana has never cheated off me. Plus, she helped me with math class. And... I like her. I don't know why Ronald's Jedi mentor would let him use other people's work. Kaminoans are supposed to be experts at cloning, maybe Ronald should clone himself and he could get twice as much work done. Or he would just cheat off twice as many people. I wouldn't mind having a clone. That way, Mr. G. could be mean to the clone instead of being mean to me...

Here you go. I just cloned some holonet articles.

Good job.

JEDI MENTOR SPOTLIGHT #3

With each Padawan studying under an individual mentor, Jedi Academy has a number of new guest Jedi teachers. In this issue, we continue our series introducing readers to two more of our visiting professors.

NORI HA is a Kaminoan Jedi whose expertise in biology and genetics is unmatched in the Jedi Order. Nori also writes the popular manners advice column "Jediquette."

Teaching for the first time, **GUB VENDO** is an Aqualish Jedi Knight, best known for his lightsaber dueling techniques to use while injured. Clumsy as a child, Vendo dedicated his life to perfecting graceful movement.

Ewok Pilot

By Roan Novachez

Roan, do you want to
draw a comic with me?

Yes ☒ ← Hey, there's only
a "yes" box and
it's already checked?

Yep! You start!

By Roan and Gaiana

Today's debate is Ronald and Lilly in favor of settlement by the Trade Federation on the moon of Endor, while Roan and Bill advocate for leaving the Ewoks alone.

As you know from our colleague Roan's comics, Ewoks are a *primitive* species that could benefit from new technology.

The benefit would clearly all be to the Trade Federation, not the Ewoks, who would be exploited along with their natural resources.

Funny you should talk about exploiting Ewoks, Roan, considering how much you profit from drawing them.

My mini-comics cost more to print than I sell them for!

Er, actually, I think the bigger picture is that in order to make the Endor moon a better place for the Ewoks, there will naturally need to be some benefit for the Trade Federation.

"Natural" is exactly the word I'd like us to remember here. The Ewok's culture would be destroyed, along with their ecosystems.

Speaking of Ewok culture, Bill, I notice, as a D.J., you steal a lot of Ewok beats.

It's called remixing!

What does Bill's music have to do with Endor? Both of you just use Ewoks.

The fact is that the Trade Federation will empower Ewok society, and lead it into a new Golden Age!

clap clap clap clap clap clap clap clap clap

I think the standing ovation shows I'm the clear winner here, Roan. It's only one person. Still, he's standing.

clap clap clap clap clap

The class somehow voted that Ronald's team won (by UNE vote) in our debate, even though what he was saying is OBVIOUSLY wrong. It didn't even feel like a debate, since mostly it was Ronald ~~interrupting~~ interrupting us to say something kind of personal. And talking about stuff that didn't have anything to do with Ewoks or the Trade Federation. Bill and I ended up spending our time responding to Ronald instead of making our points. We could have done better. Lilly wasn't happy, either, though. She

Roan, didn't you lie about the Voorpaks? Are you lying now?

Roan, how can we trust your facts, with your history of exploding science projects?

How can you claim to speak for the Ewoks? Are you, in fact, an Ewok?

apologized to us for what Ronald was

Ugh, so annoying.

I'm so annoyed.

That was soooo annoying.

saying, and for not speaking up more. It really bugged her that she didn't get to say more, and win the debate by actually...debating?

Poor Roan... still haven't gotten a new backpack?

No time. Still catching up on homework.

Well, we got you a new one!

It's neon green!

With a baby Ewok attachment!

Because you like Ewoks!

Oh, yeah... it's... great. Uh, thanks, guys.

Kind of small, too...

Don't you like it?

Uh, no, I love it! It's great! Heh.

Just kidding, Roan! Here's the backpack we really got for you!

You guys are cruel. But also the best!

We thought you could give the other one to Ollie.

FROM: MR_GARFIELD_THE_6TH
TO: PADAWAN CLASS GROUP
SUBJECT: OSSUS VISITING
STUDENTS!

OPTIONS
◀ REPLY
▶ FORWARD
▣ PRINT
⦿ POST TO HOLOBOOK

ATTENTION, ALL CORUSCANT JEDI ACADEMY STUDENTS!

THIS WEEK, STUDENTS FROM THE OSSUS JEDI ACADEMY OFF-CAMPUS EXPLORER PROGRAM WILL VISIT OUR SCHOOL! SINCE LILLY KNOWS THEM, SHE WILL ACT AS THEIR GUIDE, BUT DURING THIS VISIT, ALL STUDENTS ARE EXPECTED TO ACCOMMODATE OUR GUESTS!

YOU WILL BE REPRESENTING OUR SCHOOL, SO PLEASE DON'T MAKE ME FIND NEW WAYS TO MOTIVATE YOU TO BEHAVE WITH RESPECT, OR YOUR FAILURE WILL BE COMPLETE!

AND I DON'T WANT TO HEAR ANY COMPLAINING! HMPH!

At first, we were all intimidated by the other kids from Ossus. We played some soccer and they were all awesome. Some of them are even better than Lilly! Then, they sat in on our math class and ~~aparently~~ apparently are way ahead of us because they already knew all the equations we were working on.

I tried to lift a rock with the Force, but smelled a sock, of course.

They weren't jerks about it, though. And we realized there were some things we do better, too. We were writing poems in creative writing class, and even they knew some of what they wrote was pretty bad. Cronah tried to make fun of them, but they just laughed <u>with</u> him. That's the coolest thing about them —

← totally annoyed

they know they aren't the best at everything, but don't worry about it. They just ~~concintrate~~ concentrate on what they do well. And they all work together, instead of trying to beat one another at everything.

How'd you get that shade of blue on your lightsaber, Roan? Mine keeps turning muddy yellow.

YEAR OF THE VISITORS ENDS

Jedi Academy was even more crowded last week as students from the Ossus Campus visited the Coruscant Campus, which was already crowded with visiting Jedi professors. Fortunately, long lines for the bathroom were infrequent and the biggest problem seemed to be Jedi and Padawans stepping on one another's robes. Master Yoda was

happy with the visit, declaring, "the merrier, the more! Heh heh." Mr. Garfield was less excited. "Hmph, don't we have enough kids getting into our stuff?" he asked Master Yoda. "Harumph," he added once the visitors left.

Ewok Pilot   By Roan Novachez

Panel 1: I'm surprised how well Ewok Pilot is handling the visit from Jawa Pilot's friends. / I'd say so.

Panel 2: Bont! / Bom'loo!

Panel 3: That's my starship, not Ewok Pilot's, isn't it? / I'd say so.

THE PADAWAN OBSERVER   VOL. MXIV #7

Bill, you got a new outfit?

Oh, yeah.

I spilled some of Gammy's cooking on my old outfit, and you know those stains never come out.

Hey, guys.

Nice new outfit, Egon!

This? Oh, yeah, my old robes had a big hole in them.

Hey, guys!

New outfit?

Yeah, my mom just happened to send this to me...

I see all of you are wearing Ossus style robes. Me, too!

Aren't we cool?

I'm going to go change clothes.

Me, too.

Yep.

QUADDAY

This year so far has been great. Gaiana might actually be my girlfriend! Pasha laughed at me, because we were talking and I said I wasn't sure if Gaiana and I were really dating, or just good friends hanging out. He and Bill pointed out all the things Gaiana and I do, which made me sound silly.

1. Hold hands

2. Share blue milkshakes

3. Stare at each other for hours

4. Basically do everything together

But I'm nervous, because whenever I think everything is good is usually when I mess stuff up. Even when I'm trying hard to do everything right, I goof up or someone else (like CRONAH) trips me up. Every year I've been at Jedi Academy, something has gone horribly wrong! This year it'll probably be my independent study with Mr. G. Yesterday he was teaching me about connecting cables, but when I did it there was a loud "BOOM" and all the lights went out. So I blow something up every year, too.

ARC-170 ... RD SAFETY

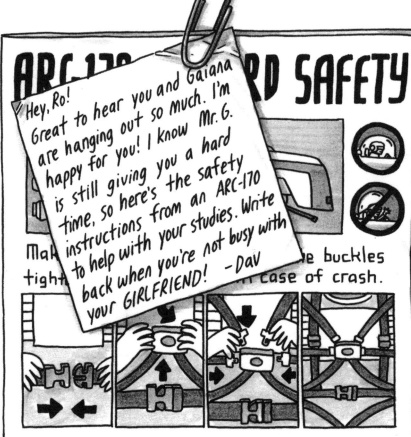

Hey, Ro!
Great to hear you and Gaiana are hanging out so much. I'm happy for you! I know Mr. G. is still giving you a hard time, so here's the safety instructions from an ARC-170 to help with your studies. Write back when you're not busy with your GIRLFRIEND! —Dav

Make ... tight ... the buckles ... case of crash.

In the event of ejection into outer space, DO NOT scream. No one will hear you, and you cannot breathe in space.

CORRECT

INCORRECT

Hey, Roan. I'm going to go meet Shi-Fara.

I'll come with you.

She's doing some focus training with Master M'Ba-Tee.

What's her focus, anyway?

Multitasking.

Hi, Pasha! Hi, Roan! I'll be done in a few minutes.

Bew! Bew!

Have you figured out what you're focusing on for individual training?

Not yet.

Principal Mar told me I should keep meditating about it.

Maybe that could be your focus—meditation!

Hmmm...

What's Pasha doing?

His homework.

✫ JEDI ACADEMY ✫ ✫ TALENT SHOW ✫

Start preparing now! What's your secret ability? Share yours with your fellow Padawans at the Jedi Academy Talent Show!

⭐ Use the Force (if you want to).

⭐ You will have 5 minutes maximum. If you are not done, loud annoying music will start playing until you leave the stage.

⭐ No smoke, fire, or pyrotechnics please.

⭐ Have fun, and don't be afraid of being embarrassed!*

⭐ For A/V needs, contact Bill as soon as possible.

⭐ Grand Prize: Replica Jedi Medallion, presented by Ronald Rinzler, Student Council President and emcee.

*By appearing in the Talent Show, you consent to having your performance holorecorded and posted to Holobook.

I know Jedi are supposed to be prepared for all kinds of situations, but how often will seven-foot-tall Wookiees toss us through the air at lightsaber-wielding foes? Because that was today's class exercise.

Another fun game: Guess Who is More Terrified!

The weird thing is that even though it sounds CRAZY (okay, it IS crazy), when we did the exercise all of our Jedi training kicked in. No one even got hurt, except Greer. But that happened when we were doing our warm-up stretches, so it doesn't count. We had to train extra-hard, too, because we're going on an overnight trip and won't have regular classes for a couple days. Master Yoda was inspired by the Ossus students' visit, so he wants us to stay in downtown Coruscant. I bet the guest Jedi mentors actually thought of it, because they want a break.

Yesterday sucked because I was stuck with Cronah all day and didn't get to take any of the notes I was supposed to. We didn't even do anything interesting, but Cronah was acting like he was cool. Pasha and Gaiana are way cooler, and they don't even try. Maybe they're cooler BECAUSE they don't try?

Look at me!

I still try, because every time I just try to be myself, I look ridiculous. I should listen to Master Yoda, and try not. Today we switched groups, and I joined up with Pasha, Gaiana, and Tegan. We went to CoCoTown, which sounds like a kids' playground, but is actually the Collective Commerce District. It's full of "exclusive" stores, that just sell stuff you can buy at other stores for less. Themed diners are also popular there, so we made a game of trying to visit as many as possible. We gave up by the time we got to the third one. It's way more fun being with a group that feels like a team.

Starship-themed diner

Ewok-themed diner

Hutt-themed diner

TRIDAY

Not only do I have Cronah and Mr. G. out
to get me, but now Ronald is starting
to annoy me more than ever. The worst
part is the way he cheats. He makes
it pretty impossible to get him in
trouble. He's a total
slimeball. Maybe he's
not an <u>actual</u> slimeball,
but I still have the
urge to wash my
hands every time he talks to me. Even
when he seems like he's being an
okay guy, he's slimy. He apologized to me
for cheating (again, since it's not the
first time). He said he's trying to be
better, but it's hard when everyone
else is so much smarter than him.
He's just looking for ways to not have
to work hard. I think
deep down inside he
believes that <u>he's</u>
the one who's smarter
than everyone else.
At least he's not as
bad as Cronah...

Hiiiiiiii,
Roannnnnn

Roan, will you autograph
this Ewok Pilot? I'm
scrapbooking all your
comic strips.
Er, okay.
I'm a
big
fan!

Here you go, Voorpee, I'll see you tomorrow.

Roan! Are you taking care of Voorpee?

Yeah, why?

I just saw him in the chemistry lab!

Voorpee! How did you escape?

Back into your home you go!

Roan! I just saw Voorpee in the cafeteria!

Huh?

Okay, all locked up. Stay here, Voorpee!

Roan! Did you leave Voorpee on the soccer field?

How could Voorpee have gotten that far so fast?! It's impossible!

I JUST put him in his cage! Which was double-locked!

Hey, Roan, Voorpee is loose in the gym. You better go get him.

Cronah's newest prank is the worst! He kept letting Voorpee out of his cage, and moving him all over the place. So I ended up spending half of today tracking down Voorpee. I don't know how Cronah did it. Maybe he's actually gotten smarter. Or someone is helping him. I would think Cyrus was pulling off the prank with Cronah, but Cyrus has been acting different this year. Maybe he's only pretending to be nice so Lilly likes him.

flinch
flinch

She must not realize how mean he can be. Unless it's not an act and Cyrus really has come back from the dark side! I tried to talk to Master Yoda about Cronah, but he was busy training Cyrus. Even if I thought it would help, I couldn't talk to Mr. G., either, because Ronald was talking with him for almost an hour. Well, it was more Ronald talking to Mr. G., because all I heard Mr. G. saying was "Hmph."

When I did finally talk to him, Mr.G. gave me a speech about how he'd been expecting me to watch Voorpee more carefully this year, and he didn't want to listen to my explanation of what happened. What's frustrating is that I already expect a lot of myself, and I didn't need Mr.G. lecturing me. I'm putting a lot of pressure on myself because I want this to be the best year ever, but it was easier when I was new and everyone ~~asumed~~ assumed I was going to fail. Not everyone, because Pasha and Gaiana have always been really helpful and believed in me. I'm lucky to have them as friends because without them, I probably would fail. I just need to survive having Mr.G. as a teacher.

Ow! You dropped a rock on my foot!

Sorry! Ha ha!

It's okay, you're new! Ha ha!

THE GOOD OLD DAYS!

Chyasse?

kurruzza, eyeta!

They're becoming a good team. I think they're actually going to fix that.

You do realize they break more stuff as a team, don't you?

Hey, Dav, how's it flying?

 Good, Ro, how's the Academy for Force-talented kids?

 It's okay. I just feel worried a lot...

 Why? Are you getting bad grades?

 No, I'm even doing okay in my independent study with Mr. G.

 Is it Gaiana? She didn't dump you already, did she?

 What? No, things with her are great. [and why would she dump me??]

 So what's to worry about? Are Cronah and Cyrus still out to get you?

 Cronah is, yeah. I'm not sure about Cyrus.

 There you go! What you're feeling is just normal, growing-up anxiety.

 So even you've felt like this?

 Me? Of course not, but I'm special. You're just totally normal.

JEDI ACADEMY TALENT SHOW
PERFORMANCE ORDER

- Please know which act you follow. Be ready to start as soon as the act before you is on stage. Remember, all acts must be 5 minutes or less.
- Keep this handout handy for reference.

01. OPENING REMARKS: Ronald Rinzler ← *Hopefully, he talks for less than 5 minutes!*

02. JO-AHN: Shadow hand puppets

03. SHI-FARA: Yo-yo tricks

04. TEGAN AND BILL: Music and dance recital

05. ROAN AND GAINA: Voorpak tricks
↑ Ugh, nice typo, whoever typed this up. It's Gaiana.

06. CYRUS: Hula-hoop ← *what?*

07. MARY: Poetry slam ← *what?!!*

08. CRONAH: Stand-up comedy routine
↳ Is it comedy if Cronah is the only one laughing?

09. INTERMISSION

AIEEE! It's on my head! IT'S ON MY HEAD!

Eeek!

WHAT'S GOING ON, NOVACHEZ?!

You don't want to know.

QUADDAY

The talent show was attacked by hundreds of Voorpees! One jumped on Cyrus, and he fell and broke his arm. They had to cancel the rest of the show while we caught all the Voorpees. The worst part was

that everyone was annoyed at <u>ME</u> because they thought it was my fault! It wasn't Voorpee, though. It was clones of Voorpee. I'm sure Cronah isn't smart enough to clone voorpaks, but he must have known about it. I don't know anyone else who would want to play a prank like that on me. And Voorpee! At least Principal Mar decided to let us finish the talent show the next day in the gym. Cronah had extra time to prepare his stand-up comedy, so he came up with a lot of jokes about Gaiana and me. Really, it was all the same joke, and it wasn't

Either Roan and Gaiana break up, or they're going to break <u>us</u>!

Whoa!

even funny the first time he made a "break" joke. Let's see... he said something about Cyrus needing to take a break, that he thought the phrase was "break a leg" not "break an arm," that maybe Tegan could do some break-dancing, something about spring break... soooo annoying. Cyrus wasn't even that upset about his arm getting broken, even though the school bacta tanks are under ~~maitenance~~ Maintenance

Waddaya mean, I'ma dummy?

Actual funniest act in the talent show

and he has to wear a sling and cast on his arm until after spring break. I think he's enjoying the attention, especially from Lilly. I still felt like it was partly my fault, so I was glad Gaiana didn't stay upset. She was more worried about taking care of all the voorpaks. I can't wait for spring break, because this whole semester has been an almost space-train wreck. OF COURSE someone is out to get me as soon as I stop messing things up on my own.

Roan, you're good at art. Will you draw on my cast?

STUDENT: ROAN NOVACHEZ		
LEVEL: PADAWAN	SEMESTER: FIVE	
JEDI MENTOR: MR. GARFIELD		

REPORT CARD

CLASS	NOTES	GRADE
HABITS OF USING THE FORCE [MASTER YODA]	*Good! Realize he was using the Force, Roan sometimes did not!*	A
PRACTICAL MATH [MRS. PILTON]	*Roan knows all of his numbers, they just don't always add up for him.*	B
CREATIVE WRITING [LIBRARIAN LACKBAR]	Roan's writing is always humorous, with delightful drawings!	A
ETHICS OF JEDI MIND TRICKS [PRINCIPAL MAR]	ROAN HAS ABILITY BUT LACKS PROPER CONTROL.	B-
INDEPENDENT STUDY I [MR. GARFIELD]	*ROAN DID WELL, BUT COULD STILL STUDY MORE INDEPENDENTLY.*	A-
LIGHTSABER ACROBATICS [KITMUM AND MR. GARFIELD]		
ADVANCED STAR PILOT TRAINING [MR. GARFIELD]	*NEEDS TO FINISH MAKEUP ASSIGNMENTS FOR A FINAL GRADE.*	INC.- INCOMPLETE

Was Lilly carrying Cyrus's bag?

Well, yeah. He does have a broken arm.

Plus they're definitely dating.

Definitely.

So, what are you doing for spring break?

I need to figure out my focus before I come back.

But my family will be camping the whole time. It's going to be fun.

What are you doing?

HOMEWORK.

Oh, right.

Have a good break, Mr. Garfield.

HMPH.

That was nice. He was actually happy.

You're being sarcastic, right?

No, I've learned to distinguish his different "hmphs."

The first half of this year went by SO fast. I was so busy, they must have been giving us more homework this year. Actually, I still have homework to do, even though it's break, because of all my work getting ruined

I think Ewok Pilot might need a break.

ZZZZZZZZ

when SOMEONE took my backpack, who I will not name, except to say that it was totally CRONAH. So my spring break will only be partly a break. At least I have an excuse to not have to work in the garden here as much. Jedi Academy spring breaks have never gone well for me. So far I had one where I just did chores and sat around bored, one

Roan, you are Jedi Master!

I wish!

where I almost lost my best friend, and now one where I'm just doing homework. Still, I get to hang out with Ollie and Dav, and Dad will be home in a couple days.

TRIDAY

I'm glad Dav and Dad got here in time to help me with my homework. Of course, they still made me do it all myself, but they both checked it and made sure I wasn't making any huge mistakes. It's not so much that it took less time, I just felt less anxhus ~~anxhus~~ anxious and stressed about getting all the work done. We did have time to do something as a family, even if it was just visiting the Museum of Tatooine in Bestine. It was a lot of fun, a little bit because I hadn't visited there in a long time, but mostly because Ollie had NEVER been there. He was so excited, I thought he was going to pass out!

I think you missed a part of one question.

Where? On that page.

But where?

Keep looking,

Just tell me!

It's going to eat me! Aaaahh!

ANCIENT KRAYT DRAGON SKULL

Hey, Gaiana! How was Naboo? Did you get the voorpaks to the zoo?

Naboo was good, but the zoo couldn't take the voorpaks.

Oh, no, that's bad! What are you going to do?

Fortunately I found a Voorpak Rescue Organization.

Oh, good! So they'll find a home for them?

They couldn't take all of the voorpaks, though.

Oh, no?

But I talked to my parents and they said I could keep one.

Oh, good! You keep making me worried.

Hee hee, I know! How has your break been?

It's been okay. Kind of like school, because I have my homework to do.

I'm sorry. At least if you're caught up, we can hang out more! I miss you.

!! ... I miss you, too.

STUDENT: ROAN NOVACHEZ
LEVEL: PADAWAN SEMESTER: SIX
HOMEROOM: MASTER YODA
CLASS SCHEDULE

0730-0850: RECKONING WITH THE FORCE
Master Yoda will teach students how to reckon with forces to be reckoned with by using the Force.

0900-0950: PUZZLE SOLVING
Students will use logic and creativity to study problem solving with Mrs. Pilton.

1000-1050: CLASSICS OF GALACTIC LITERATURE
Librarian Lackbar will guide the students in reading important books they should've read already.

1100-1150: INDEPENDENT STUDY II
Students will continue intense, individual studies with their Jedi mentors.

1200-1300: LUNCH BREAK

1300-1350: PRINCIPLES OF LIGHTSABER DEFENSE
Mr. Garfield will instruct students on parries, counterattacks, and other lightsaber defenses.

1400-1450: SENTIENT SPECIES COMMUNICATIONS
Principal Mar will show students how to communicate with species that mumble

1500-1550: EXTREME JEDI GYMNASTICS
Students will risk embarrassment, injury, and pain to learn difficult new moves with Kitmum.

PENTADAY

I was surprised to see Gaiana when I got back here, because she never said anything to me about getting braces, but it's because she feels embarrassed. I told her that, considering how often I do something awkward and embarrassing, she'll be lucky if anyone notices her braces.

Roan, I think you sat on...something?

Huh?

Mostly, I bet she's worried about kids like Cronah. So hopefully he just keeps picking on me. If he's going to pick on anyone, at least. I wonder when he's going to stop paying so much attention to me and start worrying about himself. He's always putting other people down to make himself look better, even though half the time he doesn't really look any better. If anything, he looks like a bigger jerk.

YEAH! You stink as a goalie!

Do you want to tell him he was offsides, or should I?

WHY I WANT TO BE A PILOT
By Roan Novachez

GLAD YOU'RE FINALLY THINKING ABOUT THIS.

A−

My dad is a pilot, so ever since I was a little kid, I wanted to be a pilot like him and my brother. The first time I flew in a starship, I was four years old and my dad let me steer. Not really, but he let me hold on like I was steering, and that was the coolest, best feeling I've ever had.

My friends and I always practiced on flight simulators in elementary school, and I was always one of the top students. My dad gets to help a lot of people as a pilot. Even service pilots are pretty helpful, so if I become a really good pilot I can help a lot of people, too. Besides, Tatooine is hot and boring, and I'm not good at farming. So I want to be a pilot.

DUODAY

The more I work with Mr. G., the weirder he seems. I'm not sure what difference it makes to him **WHY** I want to be a pilot? It's just one of those teacher things where they want you to think about something, but they don't tell you how it's supposed to help you. I'm sure this is just his way of messing with me. Like the other day, he told me I was going to fly the simulator for a transport escort exercise, but it was

> A crash-landing is just a crash, not a landing.

> Hmph.

actually a space station docking exercise. So I studied the wrong manual and kept crashing. Then Mr. G. also tells me I'm making a lot of progress. He won't tell me what grade I'm on track to get, though. He just tells me, "Hmph, don't worry about it."

> One of many tools for a Jedi, the Force is. Heh heh!

Which makes me worry about it even more. At least my other training is going well. Maybe I'll become the first Jedi starship mechanic.

Stuff Yoda Said This Week

Roan, can you help me? I need to print my paper, but it's not working.

Sure! It's due tomorrow, so I want to be all done so we can hang out after class today.

Hm, let's see. Just click this and this, and there we go.

TAK TAK

It's not printing.

Yeah, see?

These are all plugged in...

Did you try resetting all of the settings?

Yeah.

Reboot the programs?

Yep.

Reconfigure the configurations?

I re-re'ed everything.

I'm very confused. I thought Gaiana was REALLY angry at me, because we were supposed to hang out yesterday, but after I may (or may not) have deleted her whole paper, she didn't want to hang out. At least, that's what I assumed, because she was all "I can't hang out with you now," and acted super-distracted. Then she didn't sit by me for breakfast. Well, she didn't sit by anyone, because she didn't come to breakfast before class, but still. Then, today after class, I was ready to make it up to her. I drew a little apology note, and got her a holodata backup to use, but before I even gave those to her, she was happy to see me and wanted to hang out. I didn't realize that even Jedi can be confused by the opposite gender...

What Gaiana Says →

I can't hang out with you.

I need your help.

I'm not angry with you.

I don't know what happened.

What she → means?

Let's hang out!

I don't need your help.

I'm just really annoyed.

What did you do?

Almost there...

OBJECTIVE REACHED

TIME 04:29s
DAMAGE 0.032%
BONUSES +127

MISSION COMPLETE

Good work, Roan.

Here it comes.

That was nearly flawless.

But...let me guess.

I managed to get minimal damage, but took longer than my best time record.

I missed over a dozen bonus points.

And my helmet strap was one level of tightness off of regulation.

You can always do better, of course, but don't let that take away from what you accomplish.

Who are you and what did you do with Mr. G.?

JEDI O.C.T. [Obstacle Challenge Trial]

All Padawans must finish course to complete training at Jedi Academy. Use this plan to practice and prepare!

START →

1 SECRET ENTRANCE
Use Force to find

2 ROLLING BLOCKERS OBSTACLE

4 TALL WALL OBSTACLE

3 ROPE SWING

6 MUD PIT

5 BOOBY TRAP PATH
* Only one path will avoid triggering booby traps

7 STONE BLOCK CHALLENGE

8 KEY IN A HAYSTACK PUZZLE

9 HURDLE RACE

ANY FAILED OBSTACLE WILL SEND YOU BACK TO THE START

FINISH

HEPTADAY

I thought I was going to be ~~autfomaticly~~
automatically prepared for the physical part
of the Obstacle Challenge Trial. Everyone else
made practice look easy. As soon as I stop
focusing, though, I mess up right away. It's
not that I can't do it, or even that I'm not
good at that stuff, but I just need to pay
attention and work at it. I bet the
mental side of it will be easier.

I've always been good
at puzzles and games.
I'm one of the best
players at holochess.
Too bad my brain isn't
a muscle or something.
The exciting thing is

Nice move, Roan!

Blush

that we get to choose our teams for a
change, so I won't get stuck with Cronah. He'd
probably be happy to fail the test just to
make _me_ fail. I'll be on a team with Gaiana,

Will learning how to do a
somersault really make them
better pilots?

Probably not, but
them seem to enjoy it.

Utinni!   Yub yub!

Pasha, and Shi-Fara.
Being on a team
with them makes
me a lot less
worried about
passing this test.

Hey, Roan! Can I ask you something?

Yeah, sure.

What was that defensive move you used in your lightsaber duel last year?

When Pasha attacked from above?

You block like this...

...then swing up to try and catch your opponent off guard.

Oh, yeah. Thanks for showing me.

No problem.

It's good to have a plan for defense, you know what I mean?

Uh, yeah.

I have no idea what he means.

If someone is out to get you, you should be ready to defend, got it?

Yeah, totally.

Is he trying to warn me, or threaten me?

REMINDER

Students must have Space Pox vaccinations up to date this year.

*not actual size

OPENS NEXT HEXADAY
CORUSCANT GALLERY OF MODERN ART

KEFF D'IRST

EXHIBITION OF NEW ARTWORKS

JOIN US FOR AN ICE CREAM SOCIAL

All-natural ice cream made by the students!

On The Jedi Academy Front Lawn. Pentaday

Presented By The Cooking Club

PLEASE DO NOT PLACE ICE CREAM ON TOP OF DROIDS

EWOK PILOT

By Roan Novachez

You two have to patrol while my spaceship is being repaired.

Mambay. Acha.

Na goo! Sabioto!

BOOM!

The good news is they stopped the space pirates.

They're back? Where are their starships?

AAAAAARRRRRGGGGGHHHHH!!! If Jedi aren't supposed to give in to their frustration, can they at least write about it? This SHOULD be the best year of Jedi Academy Middle School, and basically it is, but Cronah is keeping it from being perfect. HE IS ALWAYS MESSING WITH ME. Of course he doesn't admit to anything, and I can't prove it. At the Ice Cream Social, someone poured mite sauce and beetle jelly and other gross stuff into the ice cream (when I

It couldn't have been me, Mr. Garfield. I was over there. I'm training to be a Jedi, not a Magician!

HMPH.

happened to be scooping it). RW-22 also identified fish, radish, and insect paste in the ice cream. IF it wasn't Cronah, who was it? No one else has given me a hard time every day since I first got here. Not even Cyrus. I wonder if there'd be a kid just like Cronah at Plant School if I ended up there.

Oh, was this your final project, Roan? I thought it was weeds.

CLASSICS OF GALACTIC LITERATURE

✳ Write summaries of 3 books

The Count of Mon Calamari

The story of a Mon Calamari sailor falsely held prisoner on an island by Quarren. Escapes by swimming away and uses analytic skills to plot revenge.

The Call of the Force

Story is about tauntaun named Buck that is rescued from abusive owners by a Jedi on ice planet Hoth.

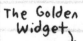

The Golden Widget

Charlie and the Droid Factory

Tells the story of a young Jawa named Charlie who wins a tour of a droid factory and then gets to take over running it.

holomail

FROM: P_Mar
TO: Padawan Class Group
SUBJECT: Obstacle Challenge Trial

OPTIONS
◄ REPLY
▷ FORWARD
▣ PRINT
● POST TO HOLOBOOK

Good afternoon, students.

Instead of regular classes tomorrow, all Padawans are required to take the Obstacle Challenge Trial. Each four-student team will have one half hour to complete the course. If you fail an obstacle, your team will need to restart the course. No further guidance will be given regarding how to get past obstacles, so your team will need to figure out the solution for each challenge without help.

May the Force be with you,
Principal Mar

P.S. Failure to complete the O.C.T. will result in having to repeat this year at Jedi Academy. Of course, I have faith that all of you will pass, so you may refrain from worrying.

TRIDAY

I'm getting nervous about the Obstacle Challenge Trial. What if I <u>DO</u> fail, and I have to stay at Jedi Academy another year while everyone else gets to move on? I wasn't stressed about this test before, because it seems pretty easy. I thought maybe that's why you have to repeat the year if you fail, because if you can't do something THAT easy, you're not ready for more Jedi training. Now I'm not sure I AM ready for more Jedi training. Jedi aren't supposed to get nervous, are they? That could be the real test: The teachers want to try and make us nervous so they can tell who doesn't really belong. I should get some sleep now, but I need to stop thinking about tomorrow first.

Think Think Think
Think Think
Think Think Think
Think
Think
Think
Think

Neetuhl?

Huh? What time is it?

Ewok Pilot? What are you doing? Your mission doesn't start for another five hours!

ROPE SWING
How do we get the rope?
Use the Force!
AAAaahoooahhHHH!
8:28
TALL WALL
I've got an idea!
Hurry!
Uh-oh!
12:19
We'll catch you!
BOOBY-TRAP PATH
So what path will avoid the traps!
Only one way to find out!
CLICK!
FWIP!
Yikes!
Easy, just don't step on that spot!
Wait!
Or that spot!
CLICK!
FWOOOOSH!
Watch out for this spot, too!
FWOOP!
FWOP!
FWIP!
CLICK!
FWOOP!

PENTADAY

I felt super ~~releved~~ relieved after finishing the Obstacle Challenge Trial. I felt like: I did it! Yes! Awesome! And then I remembered we still have half of a semester left. Everyone ended up passing the test, although Bill's team almost didn't, because Egon got stuck in the mud for a while.

My team had the second best time. Lilly's team finished fastest. She

Uh-oh.

was with Cyrus, Jo-Ahn, and Silva. I was surprised that Silva was on that team instead of Cronah. I thought Cronah might be annoyed that he wasn't on their team, but when his team finished

Yeah!

Awesome!

REALLY HAPPY TO COME IN _THIRD_!

they were all cheering Cronah like he was really great or something, which Cronah LOVED. I just wish I knew why Cronah acts the way he does. He always makes sure to put down other people, so they don't look as good. That annoys me a lot, because I already know I'm not the best. I'm just happy that I'm doing well enough to not get kicked out or fail. I'd be doing even better if I didn't have to deal with Cronah (allegedly) messing with me. For some reason he's really

Oh, sorry, Roan, I ran out of invites.

Oh, no. How disappointing.

distracting to me, even when he's not doing anything all that bad. Like, he had a birthday dinner last week, and invited everyone EXCEPT me. I'm sure he didn't expect everyone to come, but he invited them just so he could NOT give me an invitation. Not that I would've gone. Even Cyrus didn't go. He said he had a lot of work to do for his independent study, but I hope the real reason is that he's finally tired of Cronah being a jerk.

The best birthday card I got last year: (from Dav)

FOR YOUR BIRTHDAY, I HIRED EWOKS TO COOK YOU DINNER!

Inside it says: "Please tell the Ewoks not to cook ME for your birthday dinner"

holomail

FROM: JA_Yearbook_Staff
TO: roan_pilot17
SUBJECT: Yearbook Photo

OPTIONS
◀ REPLY
▶ FORWARD
▣ PRINT
◉ POST TO HOLOBOOK

Dear Student,

Congratulations on nearly completing middle school! Please review your yearbook photo choices and personal information. Reply to this holomail with your photo choice, any corrections, and the number of yearbooks you would like to purchase. Remember, yearbooks make great gifts out of great memories!

Name: Roane Novacheeze
Home Planet: Tattooine

* "Not bad. Pretty good. Yes. Very good, in fact."

TRIDAY

When I first got to Jedi Academy, I thought
Master Yoda was the most confusing teacher,
because I couldn't understand what he
was saying. Now Yoda seems completely
straightforward
and Mr. Garfield
is the most
confusing. He'll
point out everything
I'm doing wrong on

Confused, look, you, hm? Heh heh heh!

an assignment, and then tell me "Good
job!" But then I'll get every answer
right on a quiz and he'll give me a
disappointed look and act like I FAILED.
So whenever I've started to feel confident
that everything is cool, I end up doing
worse on a test or paper. Which is
maybe what he wants? Like, he's just
setting me up so I'll fail. Maybe he's
even working with
Cronah — except he
gives Cronah a hard
time, too. Unless that's
also part of Mr. G.'s
plan! If I knew, then
I could try to stop him.

ROAN, I'M GOING TO
GET YOU!

A NEW
HELMET.

THAT
ONE
LOOKS
BIG.

Stuff Yoda Said This Week

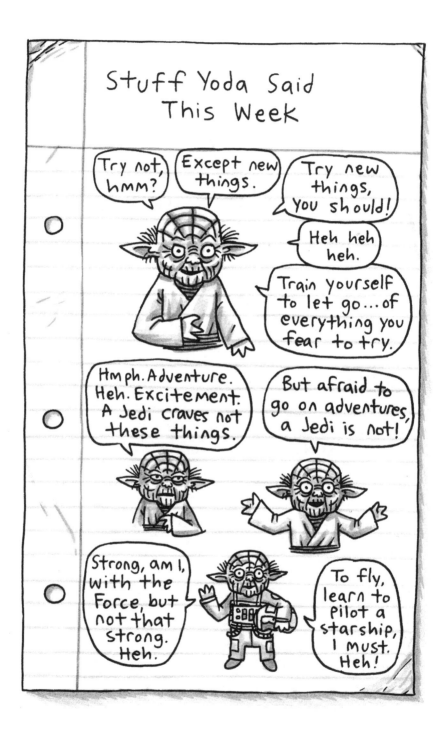

Roan, what's wrong? You look like a zombie.

Roan got a holomail that said there was training at 0400 this morning.

There was training this morning?

No, it was a prank. The message was from Master YoEa.

If I had read it closely, I would've known. Look.

"Important training, this is." Sounds real.

keep reading.

"For your butt, this training is. Many farts, you will have."

Giggle!

Poor Roan, I'm sorry! We'll help you get through the day.

Here's a napkin.

SPLAT!

Pasha took so long to decide what he was going to focus on, he has to do some catch-up work. He ended up choosing diplomacy, which to be honest, sounds a little boring. Principal Mar says that sometimes Jedi Knights have to negotiate using their lightsabers. Pasha asked if that didn't make it something other than "negotiating" but Principal Mar didn't answer. So this week Pasha and I practiced a lot of "negotiating." That should help me in the Labyrinth Trial, since lightsaber fencing is a big part of it. I also helped Egon with his studies. He's studying programming—

We probably shouldn't yell "Watch out!" before we attack.

What does this button do? Ooh! What happened? How do I do this?

so he actually found a way to make his focus playing video games! He needed a playtester for showing the game he created to his Jedi mentor. I'm not great at video games, but I think it helped.

holomail

FROM: master_yoda_642
TO: Padawan Class Group
SUBJECT: Labyrinth Trial

OPTIONS
◀ REPLY
▶ FORWARD
■ PRINT
● POST TO HOLOBOOK

For the Labyrinth Trial, helpful, this map will be. Memorize it, you should! Bring it with you, you may not.

May the Force be with you!

- Master Yoda

HEPTADAY

Everyone is starting to freak out about the end of the school year coming up. Shi-Fara spent two hours writing her name, crossing it out, then rewriting it at the top of her puzzle-solving paper. Tegan mixed up all the pages of the new issue of the school newspaper and had to stop the printer and re-do it.

This must be perfect... PERFECT...

And Cyrus has been like a different person. He asked to borrow the combat remote for lightsaber practice. I would've said no, except Lilly was with him, and I felt like I had to say yes or she'd think saying no had something to do with her and not the time that Cyrus and Cronah borrowed it and broke it. This time, Cyrus brought it back in even BETTER condition. Even Gaiana has been acting strange, I think. But maybe not. I've never had a girlfriend before, so how would I know? She kept looking

Thanks, Roan! I cleaned out the hover sensor and washed the laser filters, too.

Oh, and I recalibrated the circuit levels for you...

all impatient with me, but not about
anything in particular. Or she'd ask if I
had any plans, or what I was up to later in
the week, and then she
would elbow me SUPER-HARD!

I don't know, what
are you—OOF!

I had no idea what she was
talking about until finally
she asked me if I would go
on a date with her, which is what she
wanted ME to ask HER. We've gone on a few
double dates, and we're always hanging out,
but Shi-Fara explained to me that I hadn't
gone on, like, an ACTUAL date with just Gaiana.
So we made plans but I got nervous and almost
canceled because I felt like I was going
to barf, but Pasha made me go and it was
AWESOME. We went for a picnic in the
woods by the soccer field, which normally
we can't go in without special permission,
but because Gaiana is studying nature
with Librarian Lackbar, we were allowed to.
It was the best.

she taught →
me all about
the trees

← all by ourselves!

delicious sandwiches
AND brownies

It was a
hot day,
but
perfect
in the
shade

spent most of the
time staring at each other and smiling

144

EWOK PILOT: UNLEASHED By Roan Novachez

It wasn't as traumatic as when my backpack was filled with food, but the latest prank played on me was still pretty frustrating. I went back to my dorm room during lunch break and someone had put grease on my door. When I tried to open it, I got grease all over my hands. I tried to wipe my hands off on my clothes but that just got it all over my clothes, too. I still couldn't open the door, because it was too slippery. One of the guest Jedi mentors saw me and let me borrow clothes, which was totally embarrassing. Especially because a bunch of the grease got in my hair, but I couldn't finish cleaning up until after my last class of the day. Of course Cronah said he didn't do it. He said he COULDN'T have done it, because Mrs. Pilton was giving him a test all morning. Yeah, right. Speaking

Gaiana, do you go to a dentist, or a mechanic?

of embarrassing, Cronah says something about Gaiana's braces every time he sees her. She joked that it's nice that we have one more thing in common — Cronah being mean to us. I'm trying to be as cool about it as she is.

JEDI LABYRINTH TRIAL

For the Jedi Labyrinth Trial, each student will begin from a different starting point. You will then find your way to the exit. Whenever you encounter another student, you are required to face off in a lightsaber fencing match. If you encounter more than one student at the same time, you may choose which student to duel. The loser of the match will have five minutes added to their finishing time.

You will be fitted with a tracking device that will keep score for matches, wins, losses, and encounters with other students. Losing three matches or taking more than one hour to complete the labyrinth will result in failing the semester. You are allowed only to bring your lightsaber with you. Be sure to eat a good breakfast, because no snacks will be allowed in the labyrinth due to the new carpet.

150

BEEP!

NO!!

This isn't fair!

You got what you deserved, Cronah. Where are your friends now?

You don't have to gloat, Roan.

I'm not. I'm just glad you finally got payback for being such a jerk.

You're as much of a jerk as anyone. Where's your payback?

I knew Cronah had to be the one messing with me, and I knew Ronald is slimy, but I didn't realize they were working together to make me miserable. I actually feel kind of sorry for Cronah now. I know how he feels... thinking you're not any good, worrying about losing all of your friends. I'm just glad I didn't turn into a complete jerk like he was being. After the Labyrinth Trial, he at least seemed like he felt bad. A little. He told Master Yoda everything about Ronald cheating and all the pranks they played this year. Cronah acted like Ronald was the one who had all the ideas and was pushing him into doing stuff, but I don't know if I really believe

He must've used Jedi mind tricks on me or something.

No way! Ronald? Mind tricks? Ha!

that. Because he was honest (for once) and didn't use the map or employee shortcut, Cronah didn't get in as much trouble. He isn't graduating from Jedi Academy until he finishes a makeup summer school semester. Ronald, on the other hand, got in HUGE trouble, and they suspended him until further notice. He didn't seem too upset, like that was his plan the whole time. Principal Mar looked at

Thank you, Master Yoda!

Ronald's work from the past couple years and found he had been cheating a long time. I could have told them that. The cool thing is that, since Ronald cheated in the Labyrinth Trial, he was disqualified— so Gaiana finished first! She works so hard and never complains. She really deserved that. They gave her a

I'm blinded!

Me, too!

cool medal for first place. We both agreed that it was a little too shiny. I finished in sixth place, which I feel pretty good about. Tomorrow, there's an end-of-the-year party. We'll all celebrate graduateing graduating from middle school. I can't believe that now when I say "It's over" it's not because I have to transfer to plant school.

Too embarrassed to stick around for the graduation party, Ronald?

No, I've got orientation at the new school I'm transferring to.

What school is it, cheater Academy?

Actually, it's my dream school: the Galactic Senate Academy! They were really impressed by my work here at Jedi Academy.

Hmph. Your work? Or everybody else's?

Ha, good one, Roan! You're right, though, I couldn't have done it without you. I'll make sure to thank you when I'm ruling the galaxy...

Please don't.

...and remember to vote for me!

Is he serious?

Uh, I think so.

The Padawan Observer End-of-the-Year Awards!

Best Student	Highest Flying	Best Friend

Most Rhythmic	Greenest	Biggest Heart

Best New Talent	Most Surprising	Most Mistaken for a Trash Can

Best Victory Dance	Least Likely to Laugh	Best Comic

Most in Need of a Haircut	Quietest	Best at Making Faces

Future Sith Lord	Toughest	Cuddliest

Jedi Academy

This certifies that

Roan Novachez

has completed the Padawan Course
of study prescribed by the Jedi
Council of the planet Coruscant
and is therefore entitled to this

Diploma

In Testimony whereof, we have
here unto affixed our signatures.

PRINCIPAL MAR
_____
Master Yoda   Principal
_____
            Homeroom Instructor
MR. GARFIELD
_____
                Jedi Mentor

DUODAY (Best Duoday ever!)

I DID IT. It's official! I got my diploma. I actually completed Jedi Academy Middle School. I spent most of the past three years thinking I might fail, but when I look back now, I don't know why I worried so much. It wasn't always easy, but it was usually fun. I also thought I wouldn't make any friends, but I made the best friends ever. And Gaiana kissed me. ON THE LIPS. I can't even tell Dav about that, or it'll be next year before I hear the end of it. Plus, I'm a pilot! Sort of. I can't fly

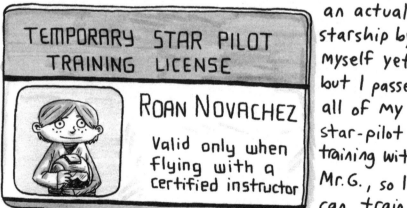

TEMPORARY STAR PILOT TRAINING LICENSE

ROAN NOVACHEZ

Valid only when flying with a certified instructor

an actual starship by myself yet, but I passed all of my star-pilot training with Mr. G., so I can train in actual starships and not just simulators next year. Last year I would've been even more nervous about the future, but now even though I know there'll be lots of challenges and new things and I'll be confused a lot of the time, I also know I can handle it. I'll miss Mr. Garfield, believe it or not. I think deep down inside he's a softie, and I'm sure he does like me. First of all, his comments on my report card were <u>all</u> positive this

CONGRATULATIONS, ROAN.

For me?

Hmph.

semester. There wasn't even a tiny "but" to any of it. Second, he gave me a graduation gift — a model of the ARC-170. And third, I thought I got assigned to Mr. G. this year either because I wanted to be a pilot and that's one of his specialties, or it was just typical random fate. But

I found out from Master Yoda that Mr. G. actually REQUESTED that I be assigned to him! And it wasn't because he wanted to torture me, but because he thought I had "real potential!" I

Proud of you, we are!

Heh heh!

wish I knew that BEFORE the school year!

MAKE YOUR OWN COMIC BOOKS!

Fold 3-4 sheets of paper in half and gather into a booklet.

Think of a story that would be fun to draw!

Plan out what happens on each page with an outline!

Make the first page your cover. What will your comic book be about?

Drawing in pencil first will make it easy to change things and fix mistakes. When you're ready, trace over the pencil lines with an ink pen.

Unfold your pages. Have an adult help you make copies.

Put the copied pages back in order, fold, and staple!

Give out copies of your comic book to all your friends!

Jeffrey Brown is a cartoonist and author of the bestselling DARTH VADER AND SON and its sequels VADER'S LITTLE PRINCESS, GOODNIGHT DARTH VADER, and DARTH VADER AND FRIENDS as well as the STAR WARS: JEDI ACADEMY series. He lives in Chicago with his wife and two sons. Despite being a lifelong Star Wars fan, he still can't use the Force, but sometimes he likes to imagine that he can.

P.O.BOX 120   DEERFIELD IL 60015-0120   USA